Carl
STAMITZ

(1745 – 1801)

Concerto No. 3 for Clarinet in Bb and Orchestra
B flat Major / Si bémol majeur / B-Dur

Clarinet / Clarinette / Klarinette

DOWANI International

Concerto No. 3

for Clarinet and Orchestra
B flat Major / Si bémol majeur / B-Dur

Clarinet in B flat

C. Stamitz (1745 – 1801)

DOW 7501

6

II 3

III 4

Romanze

Rondo

8